Race Against Time

THE STORY OF APOLLO 13

Paul May

Illustrated by Peter Dennis

OXFORD
UNIVERSITY PRESS

OXFORD
UNIVERSITY PRESS

Great Clarendon Street, Oxford OX2 6DP

Oxford University Press is a department of the University of Oxford.
It furthers the University's objective of excellence in research, scholarship,
and education by publishing worldwide in

Oxford New York

Auckland Bangkok Buenos Aires Cape Town Chennai
Dar es Salaam Delhi Hong Kong Istanbul Karachi Kolkata
Kuala Lumpur Madrid Melbourne Mexico City Mumbai Nairobi
São Paulo Shanghai Taipei Tokyo Toronto

Oxford is a registered trade mark of Oxford University Press
in the UK and in certain other countries

British Library Cataloguing in Publication Data

Data available

ISBN 0 19 919642 7

3 5 7 9 10 8 6 4

Mixed Pack (1 of 6 different titles): ISBN 0 19 919647 8
Class Pack (6 copies of 6 titles): ISBN 0 19 919646 X

Illustrated by Peter Dennis c/o Linda Rogers Associates
Cover photo by NASA

Acknowledgements
p9 NASA; p12 Digital image 1996 CORBIS; Ori/Corbis
UK Ltd.; p22 NASA/Science Photo Library; p26 Ronald Grant
Archive; p29 Sygma/Corbis UK Ltd.; p16 Apollo/NASA;
p46 NASA; p55 NASA; p60 NASA; p61 NASA;
p63 Johnson Space Center/NASA.

Printed in China

Contents

Introduction

Saturn V launch vehicle
The biggest rocket ever built.
It was 110.6 metres tall, and
weighed 2,903 tonnes.

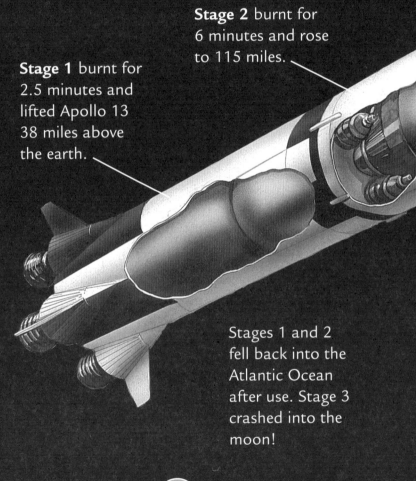

Stage 2 burnt for
6 minutes and rose
to 115 miles.

Stage 1 burnt for
2.5 minutes and
lifted Apollo 13
38 miles above
the earth.

Stages 1 and 2
fell back into the
Atlantic Ocean
after use. Stage 3
crashed into the
moon!

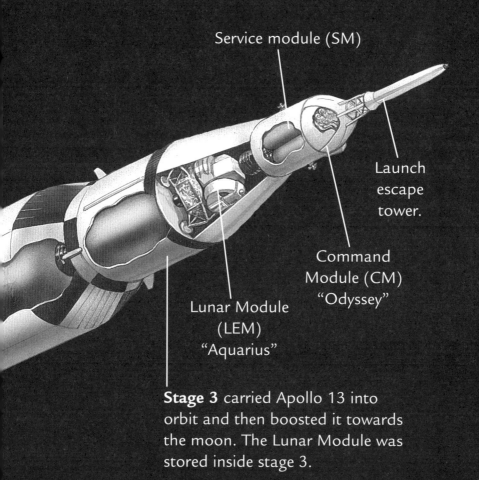

Service module (SM)

Launch escape tower.

Command Module (CM) "Odyssey"

Lunar Module (LEM) "Aquarius"

Stage 3 carried Apollo 13 into orbit and then boosted it towards the moon. The Lunar Module was stored inside stage 3.

The words that appear in italics in this story are those reported by Jim Lovell. Some are from actual transcripts, whilst others have been recalled. So as not to confuse, we have used CAPITALS elsewhere in the story to denote emphasis. See Story Background notes on p.62–63.

Apollo 8: Monday, December 23rd 1968

Jim Lovell looked out of the window of the spacecraft. There, below him, was the surface of the moon. It was only 100 kilometres away. *"It's magnificent,"* he breathed. He could see thousands of **craters** – tiny craters and enormous ones. He could see jagged mountains and flat plains. Everything was black and white. There was no colour anywhere. "What a lonely place," he thought.

Then, far ahead, something beautiful appeared – something white and green and blue and brown. The Earth was rising! The three astronauts of Apollo 8 were the first human beings ever to see the Earth rise.

Jim looked down. "I'm going to come back," he told himself. "One day, I'm going to walk on the moon."

2

Apollo 13: Saturday, April 11th 1970 1:13 p.m. Houston time

The giant Saturn V rocket stood on the **launch pad** at Cape Canaveral. Right at the top, over 100 metres in the air, was the **command module**, Odyssey. Inside, Jim Lovell was strapped into his seat. His chance had finally come. He was the commander of Apollo 13, and just three days from now he would step on to the surface of the moon.

CHAPTER 2

Jack Swigert and Fred Haise lay beside Jim in the tiny spacecraft. Neither of them had ever been in space before, but this was Jim's fourth trip. He knew it would probably be his last chance to go to the moon.

Jim felt a gentle shudder as the five rocket engines ignited and the Saturn V **launch vehicle** rose into the air. Minutes later, the spacecraft burst out of the atmosphere and into orbit around the Earth. The astronauts released

The original Apollo 13 crew

their straps, floated from their seats, and began to check their instruments. They worked for two and a half hours, and then they were ready. They fired the engines. Apollo 13 speeded up to 40,000 kilometres an hour, and headed for the moon.

Saturday, April 11th 4:32 p.m.

"*You are Go for transposition and docking,*" said the voice of Mission Control.

"**Roger**," said Jack Swigert. He was the pilot of Odyssey. Jim could see that Jack was nervous. Jim's friend, Ken Mattingley, should have been sitting there, where Jack was. But Ken was ill, and Jack had taken his place.

Jack stayed calm. This was one of the

trickiest parts of the whole mission. He pressed switches, and Odyssey separated from the rest of the spacecraft. Jack turned Odyssey around and docked carefully with the **lunar module**, Aquarius. Then he fired the engines to pull Aquarius free from the launch vehicle. The astronauts opened the hatch to the tunnel between Odyssey and Aquarius. There was a hiss and a thump.

"What was that?" exclaimed Jim. He looked around and saw Fred Haise grinning.

"Don't worry, guys," laughed Fred. "I have to press this switch now and then to keep the pressure even." Fred was the youngest astronaut. When they reached the moon, it would be his job to fly Aquarius down to the surface.

"Fine," said Jim. "Just don't do it too often, OK?"

Monday, April 13th 8.59 p.m.

A view of the moon as seen, and photographed from, Apollo 13

For two days, Apollo 13 flew on. The astronauts turned on the TV camera to beam pictures back to Earth. The moon looked bigger now, as Jim pointed the camera out of the window of Aquarius. *"We're proceeding back into Odyssey,"* Jim said, floating back towards the tunnel.

There was a thud, and Aquarius shook. Jim was startled, but then he realised what had happened. Fred was playing games again.

"*Every time he does that, our hearts jump into our mouths,*" Jim said to the TV camera. "*This is the crew of Apollo 13 signing off... Goodnight.*"

"13, this is Houston," said Mission Control. "That was a good show. And now we have some jobs for you to do."

"Go ahead, Houston," Jim replied.

"We'd like you to check your thrusters. And then we'd like you to stir your oxygen tanks."

"*OK*," said Jim. "*Stand by.*"

Inside Odyssey's **service module**, two tanks held the oxygen that kept the crew alive. The astronauts breathed the oxygen, and the oxygen did other jobs too. It mixed with hydrogen to make water, and even helped to make electricity to power the spacecraft. The oxygen was so cold that it was nearly solid, and sometimes it had to be stirred to keep it moving. Jack reached up and flicked a switch.

Ninety seconds went by. The astronauts were busy with their jobs. Fred Haise was floating through the tunnel from Aquarius. Suddenly there was a deep thud. The spacecraft shuddered. The walls moved.

Jim looked at Fred. Was this another

joke? Then he saw Fred's eyes. There was no joke. Fred was terrified. *"It wasn't me,"* he said.

Warning lights flashed on above their heads. An alarm sounded in Jim's ear. Jack stared at the instruments. He couldn't believe what he saw. Half of their power had gone. *"Hey!"* Jack shouted. *"We've got a problem here."*

The radio crackled. *"This is Houston. Say again, please."*

"Houston, we've had a problem," Jim replied.

Jim Lovell sounded calm, but all the astronauts were thinking the same terrible thought. A **meteor** must have hit them. And if a meteor had hit them, in seconds they might all be dead.

CHAPTER

Monday, April 13th 9:18 p.m.

In Houston, the controllers stared at the information on their computer screens. What they saw was frightening. Gene Krantz was the flight director. He listened to the voices of the controllers in his earphones.

"No oxygen in tank two."

"We've lost **fuel cells** one AND two."

"We've lost power."

"This CAN'T be right. There must be something wrong with the instruments."

"*OK,*" said Gene Krantz. "*Let's everybody keep cool. Let's solve the problem, but let's not make it any worse by guessing.*"

Odyssey was still shaking, rolling from side to side. Fred Haise checked the electrical circuits. Everything seemed fine. "*OK, right now, Houston,*" he said to Mission Control. "*The **voltage** is looking good.*"

Jim checked the oxygen **gauge**. "The gauge reads full," he said.

For a few seconds, the astronauts were more cheerful, and they watched their instruments carefully. But then Fred saw a needle start to fall. "One circuit has crashed," he said. "And the other one is failing, too. Soon we'll have no

power at all."

"Look at this!" said Jim. "Now the gauge says we have NO oxygen in tank two. And look at the fuel cells! Two of them are empty."

The spacecraft was still rolling madly. Jim knew he had to get it flying straight. He grabbed the controls, but the job was impossible. "I don't understand," Jim said. "It feels like something is pushing the ship."

He floated over to a window and
looked outside. And then he saw it—a
cloud of tiny, white, shining **crystals**, all
around the ship. So now Jim knew for
sure. The spacecraft was leaking. Their
precious oxygen was flowing away into
space. "There goes my chance of walking
on the moon," thought Jim. "We'll be
lucky if we make it home."

"*Houston,*" Jim said. "*We are **venting**
something into space.*"

Monday, April 13th 9:32 p.m.

Jim turned away from the window. All the oxygen in tank two had gone—but what about the other tank? He moved over to look at the gauge on tank one, and he couldn't believe his eyes. He could actually *see* the needle moving downwards. He watched for a few moments and thought quickly. If the needle kept dropping this fast, there would only be enough oxygen left on Odyssey for a few hours. And it would take them at least a hundred hours to return to Earth.

Jim showed the oxygen gauge to Fred and Jack.

"Houston," said Jack. "*Are you copying*

*that O$_2$ tank one **cryo** pressure?"*

*"That's **affirmative**,"* Houston replied.

Jim looked at the others. *"If we're going to get home,"* he said, *"we're going to have to use Aquarius."*

Apollo 13 Lunar Module (Aquarius) after separation

Back at Mission Control, a lot of people were thinking very hard. Maybe, just maybe, the lunar module, Aquarius, could bring the astronauts safely back from space. But there was a problem. Aquarius could never enter Earth's atmosphere. If it tried, it would burn away to nothing. So the scientists knew they had to save some power in the command vehicle, Odyssey, for the re-entry and landing, and they had to do it quickly. With every second, Odyssey's power was draining away.

"13, this is Houston," said Mission Control. *"We'd like you to go to your checklist. Do a Power Down."*

Jack Swigert grabbed the checklist. There was no time to waste. He began the long, difficult job of shutting down the spacecraft.

"13, Houston. Do you copy our Power Down request?"

"Roger. We're doing it right now," Jack replied.

All the time, Odyssey's oxygen was

leaking away. The spray of gas was acting like a small rocket, pushing Odyssey backwards and forwards. While Jim Lovell fought to get Odyssey under control, Jack carried on pressing switches. The ship grew darker. It grew colder, too – soon the temperature was only 15 degrees celsius. And still the needle on the oxygen gauge kept falling.

"Houston," Jack asked, *"does it look to you like the O_2 in tank one is still going down?"*

"It's slowly going to zero," came the reply.

It was a race against time. Jim Lovell and Fred Haise made their way into Aquarius. The lunar module's computers and life-support systems were sleeping, and it would take time to start them up. Back in Odyssey, Jack could see that his oxygen had nearly gone.

"13, Houston. We'd like you to start making your way over to the LEM."

But Jack Swigert wasn't ready to go to the lunar module yet. He was determined to complete his power down properly. He knew that if he didn't, they might not be able to get the ship running again. *"Fred and Jim are in the LEM already,"* he told Houston. And he carried on working.

The actor, Kevin Bacon, who played Jack Swigert in the 1995 film, Apollo 13

Monday, April 13th 10:47 p.m.

Fred, the lunar module pilot, began to
bring Aquarius to life while Jim raced
back to Odyssey. Right now, only the
computers on Odyssey knew exactly
where the spacecraft was and which way

it was facing. And, any second now, Jack Swigert would have to shut them down.

Jim copied down numbers as fast as he could. But then, even though he was good at maths, he started to worry. What if he got his sums wrong? They would be lost in space and they would never get home.

"*Houston,*" said Jim. "*I've got some numbers for you, but I want you to double check my arithmetic.*"

At Mission Control, men rushed to check Jim's results. "*OK, Aquarius,*" they said, just seconds later. "*Your arithmetic looks good there.*"

Fred started entering the numbers into Aquarius's computer. Mission Control called out instructions. The crew shouted questions to Mission Control. It was chaos. Nobody had ever done this before, and nobody was exactly sure how to do it. But at last, somehow, the two ships were ready.

Odyssey was dark – silent and cold. Jack Swigert floated through the tunnel to join Jim and Fred in Aquarius.

A film still from the 1995 film Apollo 13 shows the three astronauts looking through the window of Aquarius, the Lunar Module. Note the frozen condensation (water droplets) on the glass

CHAPTER

Tuesday, April 14th 12:02 a.m.

The crippled spacecraft flew on through
the emptiness of space. The moon's
gravity was tugging at it now. If the
astronauts simply waited, their
spacecraft would race around the moon
and head back towards Earth. But that
was no good to them. They would pass
close to Earth, but not close enough.

They would see the mountains, and the lights of the cities but they would fly on past, out through the solar system and away.

Jim Lovell knew that they would have to "burn" their engines to change their course, but he was worried. Before a burn, astronauts always checked their position by looking at the stars. And Jim couldn't SEE any stars. The explosion had left a cloud of glittering wreckage all around the ship. Jim couldn't tell the stars from the wreckage. When they made the burn, they would have to simply take a chance. It was all they could do.

"*13,*" said Houston, "*how do you feel about making a burn in 37 minutes?*"

"*We'll give it a try,*" said Jim, "*if that's all we've got. But could you give us a little more time?*"

Houston gave them one hour to get

ready. Fred raced to prepare Aquarius for the burn. The others helped when they could, but only Fred really understood how Aquarius worked. The hour seemed to pass incredibly fast. The computer display flashed. Thirty seconds to go. Five seconds to go.

"*We have ignition,*" said Houston.

Jim moved a lever and Aquarius vibrated as the engines burned faster.

"OK, *Aquarius, you're looking good,*" said Houston.

Jim held the lever steady, watching as the seconds ticked on – twenty seconds... thirty seconds... And then it was over. The computer shut down the engines, and the astronauts waited in silence.

In Houston, the controllers checked

to see if the ship was on course. They were amazed. The burn had been perfect. *"You are Go, Aquarius,"* they told the astronauts.

"Roger," said Jim. He was relieved, but he knew that there were more problems ahead of them. Aquarius was a tiny spacecraft. It held enough power and water to last two astronauts for two days, but now there were three of them squashed inside, and it would take them at least four days to get back.

Aquarius was going home, but could the astronauts stay alive that long?

Tuesday, April 14th 5:17 a.m.

The crew of Apollo 13 needed to rest. It was eight hours since the explosion, and still none of them had slept. While Jim and Jack shouted through the crackling radio, Fred Haise floated off to try to sleep. He was shocked when he arrived in Odyssey. It was so cold that he could see his breath. He shivered, then he settled into his couch. After just two hours, he floated back up to Aquarius.

"*That's it?*" asked Jim.

"*It's too cold up there,*" replied Fred. "*Too cold and too noisy. You guys can try it if you like.*"

Just a few hours later, at 6:21 p.m. Houston time, Apollo 13 flew behind the moon. As the moon hid the sun, Jim

*Oblique view of the moon's surface
showing craters and mountain ridges*

Lovell could see the stars at last. There was a blackness where the surface of the moon must be. Then the spacecraft flashed into sunlight, and the astronauts could see the craters and mountains below them. Fred and Jack rushed for their cameras, but Jim stood back and watched their excited faces.

Jim had seen the moon before. He had longed to walk down there on the surface but he knew his chance had gone. All he wanted to do now was to get home safely. Houston had told them to get ready for another engine burn. This burn would speed the spacecraft up. They would come home faster, and they would have a much better chance of staying alive. He tried to hurry the others along.

"Jim," grumbled Fred. *"We've come all the way out here – don't you think they're going to want us to get some pictures?"*

"If we don't get home," said Jim, *"you'll never get them developed."*

"Jim, you are Go for the burn," said Houston, two hours later.

"Roger, I understand," said Jim. *"We are Go for the burn."*

The engines rumbled. One minute passed, two minutes, three minutes, four... Still the ship trembled as the rockets burned.

"*Aquarius,*" said Houston, "*ten seconds to go. Five... four... three... two... one.*"

"*Shutdown!*" said Jim.

Aquarius was on course, and now the astronauts were desperate for sleep. But there was no time for sleep. Aquarius was using too much power and too much water. They had to turn off as much of the spacecraft's power as they could, and they had to do it right now. The tired astronauts started to work.

Wednesday, April 15th 3:00 a.m.

Fred Haise was alone in Aquarius. Jim and Jack were in Odyssey, sleeping. Fred looked out of the window. The moon looked smaller now. They were going home.

"Fred," said the voice from Mission Control, *"how about telling us how that CO_2 reads?"*

CO_2 is carbon dioxide. When a person breathes, their body takes in oxygen, but it also gives out carbon dioxide. And carbon dioxide is poisonous.

"*OK,*" said Fred. "*I'm reading 13 on the gauge.*"

Fred was shocked. He knew that if the gauge rose just a fraction higher they would start to feel very sick. He checked again. "*Yeah, 13,*" he said.

Aquarius had a way of getting rid of carbon dioxide from the air. It sucked air through a filter which contained a chemical that absorbed the carbon dioxide. When the filter was full, the astronauts had to change it for another one. But with three people in the lunar module instead of two, the filters filled up fast. And now the last one was nearly full.

In Houston, a scientist called Ed Smylie had been working on the carbon

dioxide problem. There were plenty of
spare filters in Odyssey, but they were
square, and the ones in Aquarius were
round! If only he could figure out a way
to fit a square filter into a round hole.
Ed Smylie set to work. He used tubes
and sticky tape and cardboard. He
worked all night and all day, and at last
he thought that maybe he had a
solution. He raced to Mission Control
with his invention. He was just in time.

"*All right,*" said Mission Control to Fred Haise in Aquarius. "*We're going to want to get started putting together the little **canister** we've come up with.* These are the things you'll need."

Jim and Jack were awake now. The temperature in Odyssey had fallen almost to zero, so they hadn't managed to sleep much. Now, they started searching for the things they needed to make the new canisters. Jack found scissors and a roll of grey tape. Jim ripped the plastic covers from the underwear he would have worn on the moon. Fred ripped out the heavy cardboard pages that told him how to fly Aquarius back from the surface of the moon. He wouldn't be needing them!

They worked for an hour, cutting and sticking, as Mission Control read out Ed Smylie's instructions. It was more like

being back at school than flying a
mission to the moon!

"*OK*," Jack said. "*Our do-it-yourself
canister is complete.*"

The astronauts crowded round the
CO_2 gauge. In Houston, the controllers

watched their screens. Then, very slowly,
the needle began to fall. 12... 11.5... 11...

The controllers smiled. The
astronauts smiled. Ed Smylie smiled.
Then they all went back to work. Apollo
13 was still a long way from home.

CHAPTER

Wednesday, April 15th 10:30 p.m.

The Earth's **gravity** had hold of the spacecraft now, and pulled it along, faster and faster. The controllers at Houston checked Apollo's course on their computer screens, and they began to worry. The spacecraft was hurtling towards Earth at the wrong angle. It would hit the **atmosphere** and bounce off it like a stone skimming off water. It would race on into outer space.

View of Earth showing the polar ice cap in the south, and Africa, very clearly

Houston called the ship. "13, *your course is a little bit shallow.* We'd like a 14 second mid-course burn."

"*Roger, understand,*" Jim Lovell replied.

"You don't have enough power to use the computer," said Mission Control. "We'd like you to control the engine with the Start and Stop switches."

"*Roger.*"

"And when you steer, we'd like you to place Earth in the centre of your window, and keep it there all through the burn."

All three astronauts had to help. Jim and Fred shared the controls. It would need both of them working together to keep the ship pointing straight at the Earth. Jack used his wristwatch to time the burn. He called out the seconds of the countdown.

"*Two minutes to go.*"

The astronauts were silent as they waited. They all knew what would happen if they got this wrong. They would either burn up in the atmosphere, or be lost in space.

"*One minute.*"

"*Thirty seconds....*

10... 9... 8... 7... 6... 5... 4... 3... 2... 1..."

Jim pressed the start button and the engine rumbled. He and Fred Haise struggled to keep the Earth steady in the window as Jack's voice steadily

counted the seconds. *"Twelve seconds...
thirteen... fourteen."*

Jim punched the Stop button. There
was silence. *"Houston, burn complete,"* said
Jim.

"OK, guys," said Mission Control. *"Nice
work."*

Apollo 13 was back on course again.

It was now late on Wednesday night.
On Friday afternoon, if all went well,
they would splash down in the Pacific
Ocean. Jim knew that steering the
spacecraft back through the atmosphere
was going to be difficult and dangerous.
But first, they would have to bring the
command module, Odyssey, back to life,
and so far Mission Control hadn't told
them how to do that.

Jim wondered if they knew how to
do it.

Thursday, April 16th 6:30 p.m.

Fred Haise was sick. He was shivering and sweating at the same time.

"*Are you all right, Freddo?*" asked Jim.

"*Yeah, sure. I'm fine. Why?*"

"*You sure don't look fine.*"

"*Well, I am.*"

Jim was worried about Fred. He was worried about all of them. They were

cold and tired. They couldn't afford to
make a mistake, not now they were so
close to home. And Jim was still waiting
for Houston to tell him how to power
up Odyssey. They were running out of
time.

Jim put down the pack of cold soup
he had been drinking, and headed for
Odyssey. Fred followed Jim into the
command module. Every surface was
covered with tiny drops of water. It was
condensation from the astronauts'
breath.

"*This is a mess*," Jim said.

There were hundreds of switches in Odyssey. There were tens of thousands of wires. Water could find the smallest crack in the insulation around the wires. It could make electricity jump from wire to wire. It could wreck the spacecraft. Jim ran a finger through the condensation. Droplets floated into the air.

"*Well,*" said Jim, "*we're not going to know a thing until we actually Power Up.*"

"*And we're not going to Power Up until they get around to reading us that checklist,*" said Fred.

In Houston, the scientists thought they had finally found a way to Power Up Odyssey.

"*Houston, Aquarius.*"

"*Go, Houston,*" said Jim.

"We are ready to read you the checklist."

Jack Swigert took the pen and paper Jim handed him, and put his headset on. It was his job to write down the instructions. It would be his job, in just fifteen hours time to throw hundreds of switches, in exactly the right order. Jack hoped he would get some sleep before then. He began to write. It took nearly three hours to copy down all the instructions.

Later, as Jack tried to sleep, he began to worry. His tired brain was racing. In his mind he could see two switches. One said SM JETT. That was the one he would press first. It would send the damaged service module attached to Odyssey flying off into space, as Jim and Fred watched from the windows of Aquarius. The other switch said LEM JETT. When Jack threw that switch, Aquarius would separate from Odyssey

and fall away to burn in the atmosphere
before crashing into the ocean.

"What if I get the switches mixed up?"
thought Jack. "What if Jim and Fred are
in Aquarius and I accidentally press the
wrong one?"

He went into Odyssey and wrote NO
on a piece of paper. Then he taped the
piece of paper to the LEM JETT switch.
That was one less thing to worry about.

But even then, Jack couldn't sleep.

Time passed. And now, with only five hours to go before they re-entered Earth's atmosphere, it was time to **jettison** the service module. Jim and Fred were ready in Aquarius with their cameras. Jack looked at the piece of paper taped to the LEM JETT switch. "Not that one," he thought. He pressed the SM JETT switch, and all the astronauts stared out of the windows.

Explosive evidence: a view of the damaged SM as photographed from the LEM/ Command Module after jettisoning

"There's one whole side of the spacecraft missing!" gasped Jim.

Tangles of wires and insulation trailed from the blackened hole.

"Man," said Fred. *"That's unbelievable!"*

They all knew that they were lucky to be alive.

CHAPTER

Friday, April 17th 10:00 a.m.

"You are Go to start Powering Up Odyssey," said Houston.

Jim and Fred waited anxiously in Aquarius as Jack climbed into Odyssey and threw the first switch. They waited for the sound of a hiss or a crackle, or the smell of burning. But all they heard was the sound of Odyssey humming slowly into life. Maybe they really were going to make it home.

Jim looked around Aquarius. The tiny lunar module had saved their lives, but now it was time to leave. *"Freddo,"* he said, *"it's time to bail out."*

Fred didn't answer. He looked awful.

"Can you hold out two more hours?" asked Jim.

"I can hold out as long as I have to," Fred replied.

"Two hours," repeated Jim. *"After that, we're floating in the South Pacific."*

The astronauts sealed the hatches between Odyssey and Aquarius. Jack ripped the piece of paper from the switch that said LEM JETT, and pressed the switch. The lunar module that had carried them more than 400,000 kilometres fell away towards the Earth.

And now the tiny command module was travelling at 40,000 kilometres an hour. The oceans and mountains were just 25,000 kilometres below. They were about to enter the atmosphere.

"I know all of us want to thank you guys for the very fine job you did," Jack told Houston.

"That's affirm," said Jim.

"I'll tell you," replied the voice from Mission Control, *"we all had a good time doing it."*

The astronauts were strapped in. They stared out of the window as they felt the force of gravity growing, pressing them back into their couches. They saw pink, then orange, then fiery red. Minutes went by, and then the red faded slowly back to orange, and suddenly there was blue sky outside.

Houston control room

In Houston, the control room was packed with people. On entering the atmosphere the crew had lost communication. The airwaves hissed as the controllers waited. Four minutes passed.

"Odyssey, Houston, standing by, over."

It was Joe Kerwin's job to talk to the spacecraft. He tried again. *"Odyssey, Houston, standing by, over."*

He tried once more, and suddenly there was a voice – Jack Swigert's voice.

"*OK, Joe.*"

"*OK,*" replied Joe Kerwin. Everyone in Mission Control was cheering and laughing. "*We read you, Jack.*"

Parachutes opened. The command module floated gently downwards out of a blue sky. There was a bump, a gentle splash, and then water was running down the windows of the spacecraft.

"*Fellows,*" said Jim Lovell, "*we're home.*"

The splashdown

Story Background

The two main sources for the text are: Lovell, J and Kruger, J, *Apollo 13*, Coronet, 1995 and *Apollo by the Numbers: Statistical Reference* written by Richard Orloff (NASA SP-4029) available on the web at **http://history.nasa.gov/SP 4029/Apollo_13a_Summary.htm**

Wherever possible when writing speech I have quoted the words spoken by the astronauts and controllers as reported in Lovell's book. Lovell and Kruger say of this speech (in the notes to their book): "...*though the in-flight conversations included in the text were taken directly from transcripts, in many cases we have edited, compressed, or paraphrased them in the interests of both comprehensibility and pacing. But in no case has the meaning or substance of any of the exchanges been changed. Other dialogue that*

was not preserved on tape or paper was
reconstructed through interviews with at
least one – and usually more than one – of the
principals involved."

There are cases in this story where
I found it necessary to alter the actual
spoken words. To make it clear where
I have done so, all speech which
is quoted without
alteration by
me is in
italic type.

Recovery of
the Command
Module from
the splashdown
site

Index

Glossary

affirmative communications term meaning yes

atmosphere a gaseous envelope surrounding a heavenly body

canister a small metal container

command module the main part of the space ship

crater bowl-shaped hollow in the moon's surface

cryo extreme cold

crystals ice-like minerals

fuel cells sources of electricity

gauge dial to measure processes on the space ship

gravity force attracting bodies towards earth

jettison dropping of objects

launch pad structure to hold the space ship during take-off

launch vehicle part of the space ship used when taking off from earth

lunar module part of the space ship which lands on the moon

meteor a small, moving body in space

Roger communications term meaning message received and understood

service module part of the space ship

venting hole through which gas escapes

voltage electromotive force